YOUR BODY

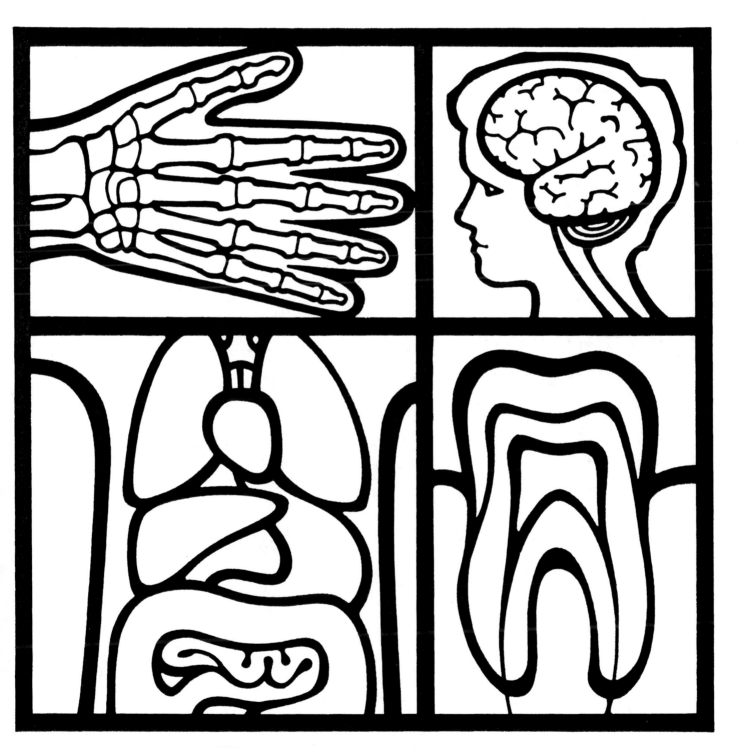

Written by Linda Schwartz
Illustrated by Beverly Armstrong

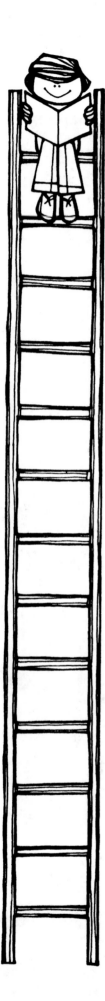

The
Learning
Works

Edited by Sherri M. Butterfield

The purchase of this book entitles the individual
classroom teacher to reproduce copies for use
in the classroom.

The reproduction of any part for an entire school
or school system or for commercial use is strictly
prohibited.

Copyright © 1990
Creative Teaching Press, Inc.
Huntington Beach, CA 92649
All rights reserved.
Printed in the United States of America

To the Teacher

YOUR BODY is a Learning Works mini-unit created especially for children in grades one through four. The purpose of this unit is to blend the presentation of facts about the human body with the practice of essential skills to produce the very best in theme-related teaching and results-oriented learning.

Information about the human body is presented in easy-to-read passages. Kids learn the names of some of the most important parts of the body. They also learn what these parts do, how they work, and how to care for them and keep them healthy. Associated activities involve children in observing and comparing, matching and classifying, identifying and labeling, ordering and sequencing, locating and using information, and following directions. These tasks are carefully designed to improve hand-eye coordination; increase skill in auditory and visual discrimination, word recognition, and spelling; stimulate curiosity; and foster creative expression.

In addition to information and activity sheets, this book also includes a page of fascinating facts about the human body, a glossary of related terms, and an **Anatomy Awareness Award**.

Although this book was created for students, the teacher has not been forgotten. For your convenience, we have included an **All-Purpose Worksheet** featuring teeth. You can reproduce this sheet, add content— vocabulary words to be looked up, spelling words to be learned, math problems to be solved—and reproduce again so that you will have one for every member of your class. A page of useful, reproducible **Clip Art** is also included.

This book also contains instructions for five **Correlated Activities** suitable for small-group or whole-class projects, two pages of **Eye Care Mini-Posters**, and **Special Human Body Awards** with which you can thank classroom helpers and recognize outstanding effort. The whimsical illustrations throughout the book can easily be enlarged, reduced, or used as is to decorate announcements, bulletin boards, fliers, game boards, invitations, name tags, newsletters, notes, and programs.

This mini-unit offers stimulating activities in an anatomical context so that young learners can strengthen their skill in essential areas while increasing their knowledge about the human body.

Contents

Your Body 5

Take a Look at Yourself . . . . (Observing) 6

About Face . . . . (Comparing and Matching) 7

Take Another Look . . . . (Observing) 8

Sounds the Same . . . . (Phonics—Vowel Sounds) 9

What Is Below Your Neck? 10

Which Is Longer? . . . . (Measuring and Comparing) 11

What's Inside Your Head? 12

How Do You See? 13

Tricky Pictures . . . . (Measuring and Comparing) 14

Eye Care Ideas . . . . (Mini-Posters) 15–16

How Do You Hear? 17

What Do You Hear? . . . . . . (Auditory Discrimination) 18–19

How Do You Smell? 20

What Do You Smell? . . . . . (Olfactory Discrimination) 21

I Smell Dinner! . . . . (Creative Writing) 22

How Do You Taste? 23

A Yucky Taste . . . . (Creative Writing) 24

Flavor Fun . . . . (Taking a Survey; Following Directions) . . 25

Flavor Favorites . . . . (Graphing; Following Directions) 26

How Do You Think? 27

Follow the Dots . . . . (Numerical Sequencing; Hand-Eye
                                  Coordination; Fine Motor Skills) 28

How Do You Chew? 29

Crossword Fun . . . . (Word Recognition and Meanings) 30

What's Inside Your Trunk? 31

What Does Your Heart Do? 32

How Does Your Blood Flow? 33

What Is Your Pulse? 34

Feel the Beat . . . . (Counting, Comparing, and Graphing;
                                  Following Directions) 35

What Are Your Lungs? 36

Body Parts Puzzle . . . . (Letter and Word Recognition) 37

Bones and Muscles 38

Fascinating Facts About Your Body 39

Human Body Clip Art 40

Teeth to Try . . . . (All-Purpose Worksheet) 41

A Few Words About Your Body 42–43

Anatomy Awareness Award 44

Special Human Body Awards 45–46

Correlated Activities 47

Answer Key 48

Your Body

Your body is made up of many parts. Some of these parts are on the outside, where you can see them. Some of these parts are on the inside, where you cannot see them.

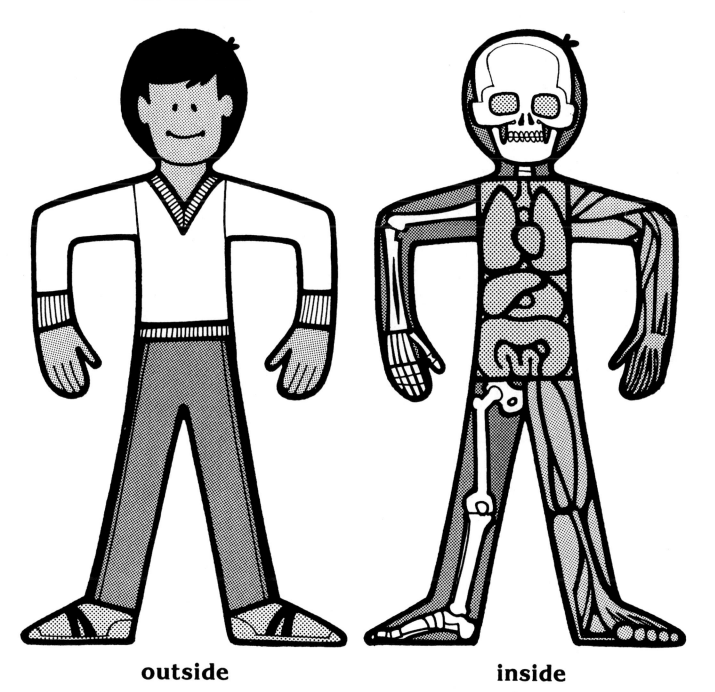

outside   **inside**

Name _____

Take a Look at Yourself

Take a good look at yourself in a mirror. Start at the top. Look at your **head**. What color is your hair? Does it touch your shoulders? Does it cover your ears? Can you wiggle your ears *without* touching them?

Look at your **face**. What color are your eyes? How does your face change when you smile? What happens when you frown? Make a funny face. Notice what your forehead, eyes, nose, lips, and cheeks do when you make this face. Stick out your tongue. Can you touch your tongue to your nose?

Name _____

About Face

Remember how your face looked when you smiled and when you frowned. Cut the squares apart and arrange them to make a picture of a face. Make it smile if you feel happy. Make it frown if you feel sad.

Name _____

Take Another Look

Take another look at yourself in a mirror. Your **neck** connects your head to the rest of your body. Tip your chin up a little bit. Watch the front of your neck when you swallow. Can you see something move inside? What you see is your **Adam's apple**. It isn't really an apple at all. It's a lump of hard stuff, called **cartilage**, that helps protect the softer things inside your throat.

Rest three fingers lightly on the front of your neck while you talk or hum softly. Can you feel your neck move a little bit? The tiny movements you feel are the **vibrations** of your **vocal cords**. These vibrations make the sounds other people hear when you talk, sing, or yell.

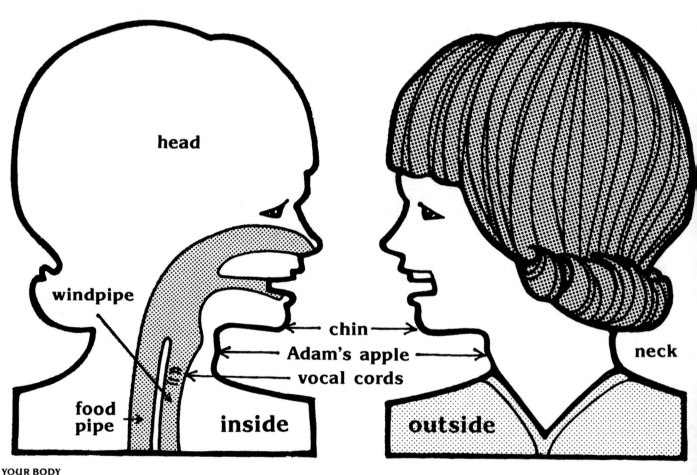

head

windpipe

food pipe

inside

chin
Adam's apple
vocal cords

outside

neck

Name _____

Sounds the Same

Look at the pictures in each row. Say the words. Put an **X** on the one picture in which the vowel sounds different. Color the three pictures in which the vowels sound the same.

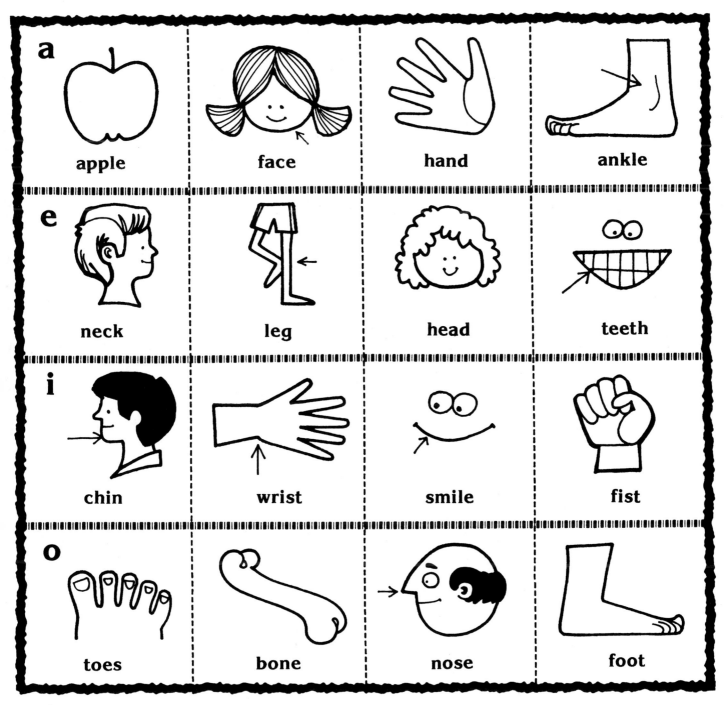

a

apple   face   hand   ankle

e

neck   leg   head   teeth

i

chin   wrist   smile   fist

o

toes   bone   nose   foot

What Is Below Your Neck?

Below your neck is your **trunk**. Your back, your chest, and your stomach are all parts of your trunk.

Your arms are joined to your trunk at your **shoulders**. Your legs are joined to your trunk at your **hips**.

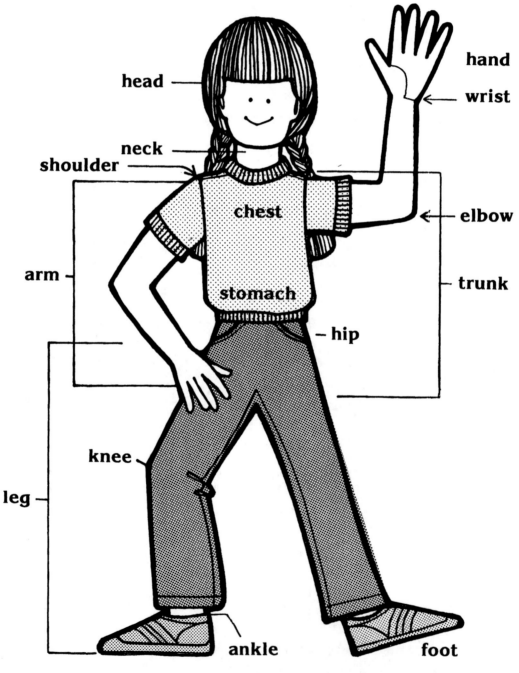

head

hand

wrist

neck

shoulder

chest

elbow

arm

trunk

stomach

hip

knee

leg

ankle

foot

Name _____

Which Is Longer?

Compare the lengths. Use a measuring tape, strips of paper, or pieces of string. Put an **X** on the one that is longer.

1. Which is longer, 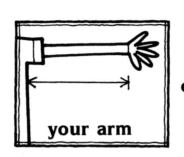 or  ?

2. Which is longer,  or 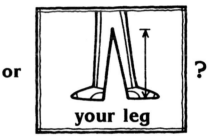 ?

3. Which is longer, 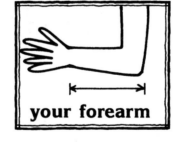 or 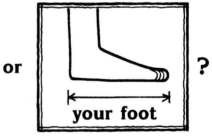 ?

4. Which is longer, 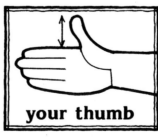 or 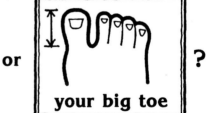 ?

5. Which is longer, 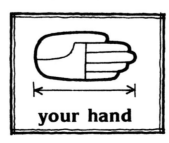 or 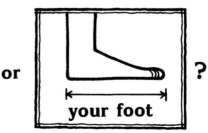 ?

What's Inside Your Head?

Inside your head are some very special parts of your body. These parts help you see, hear, smell, taste, and think. These parts also help you chew and swallow.

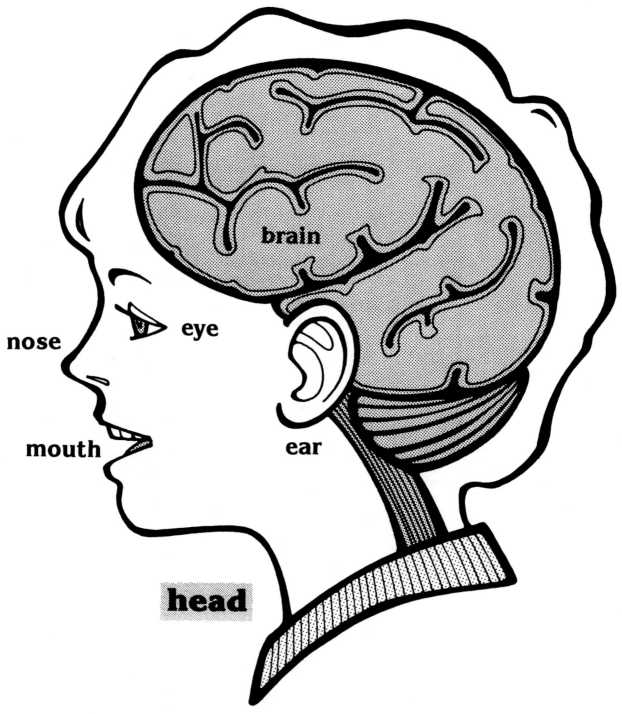

How Do You See?

You see with your **eyes**. When your eyes are open, light comes through the small black hole in the center of each eye. This hole is called the **pupil**.

The light passes through a **lens**. This lens collects the light and points it to the back of your eye. The light makes a picture of what you see on the back of your eyeball, which is called the **retina**.

The picture is carried by a special **nerve** to your brain. Your **brain** thinks about the picture. It decides what the picture is, what it means, and what you should do about it.

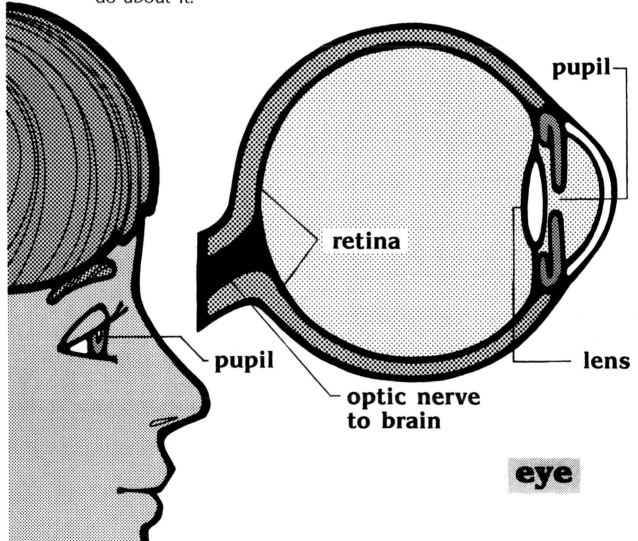

pupil

retina

pupil

lens

optic nerve
to brain

eye

Name _____

Tricky Pictures

Some pictures use your eyes to play tricks on your brain. Your eyes see these pictures clearly, but your brain misunderstands them. Pictures that use your eyes to play tricks on your brain are called **optical illusions**. See if these three optical illusions fool you.

Big Circle—Little Circle

Which center circle is bigger? Measure both center circles to find out.

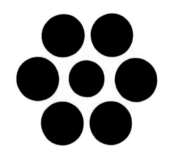

Cutting Corners

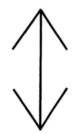
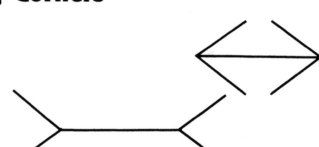

Which line in each pair is longer? Check your answer by measuring all four lines. Were you right?

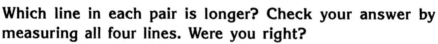

Tale of a Top Hat

Look at this top hat. Is it taller than it is wide? If so, how much taller? Measure the height and width of the hat to check your answer.

Eye Care Ideas

Watch where you're going!

Be very careful around fires.
Never play with firecrackers.

Use sharp or pointed objects with care.

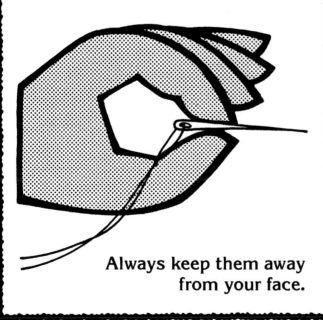

Always keep them away from your face.

When you get something in your eye, don't rub it.

Ask an adult for help.

Eye Care Ideas

Never throw anything at anyone's face.

Avoid getting soap or other chemicals in your eyes.

Never look directly at the sun.

Always avoid glare.

Wear safety glasses when you work with tools

or near flying particles.

How Do You Hear?

You hear with your **ears**. Sounds make the air ripple in waves. These waves spread out in circles from the sound that makes them. Your eyes cannot see these waves, but your ears can hear them.

The outer part of your ear is called the **pinna**. The pinna catches **sound waves** that are in the air. It sends them deep inside your ear. The waves bump against your **eardrum** and make it wiggle, or **vibrate**.

When your eardrum vibrates, it makes three tiny **bones** inside your ear vibrate also. In turn, these bones make a jelly-like **liquid** in your ear move back and forth. Hairlike **nerve ends** in this liquid feel these movements and carry them to your brain.

Your **brain** thinks about the movements. It decides what made the sound you heard. It decides whether the sound you heard was music or noise.

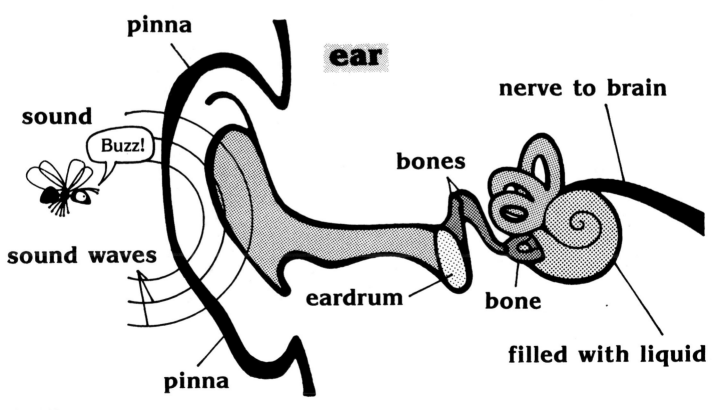

What Do You Hear?

What You Need

- at least five empty containers with tight-fitting lids (You can use film canisters, margarine tubs, or plastic eggs, but all of the containers you use should be the same size and shape. They should also be made of the same material.)
- a small amount (about ½ cup) of plastic beads or buttons, dried beans or peas, cornmeal or sand, metal paper clips or brads, and pennies or other coins
- a black felt-tipped marking pen
- masking, electrician's, or duct tape

What You Do

1. Put beads or buttons in one container, beans or peas in another container, cornmeal or sand in the next container, paper clips or brads in the next container, and pennies or other coins in the last container.
2. Use the marking pen to number the containers.
3. Create an answer key so that you will know the contents of each numbered container.
4. Tape the containers shut.
5. Make copies of the activity sheet on page 19.
6. Make the containers and activity sheets available in a **Classroom Listening Center**.
7. Tell students to shake each container and identify its contents by sound alone.

Name _____

What Do You Hear?

Shake each container. Listen to the sound. Decide
what is inside. Write a number on the line.

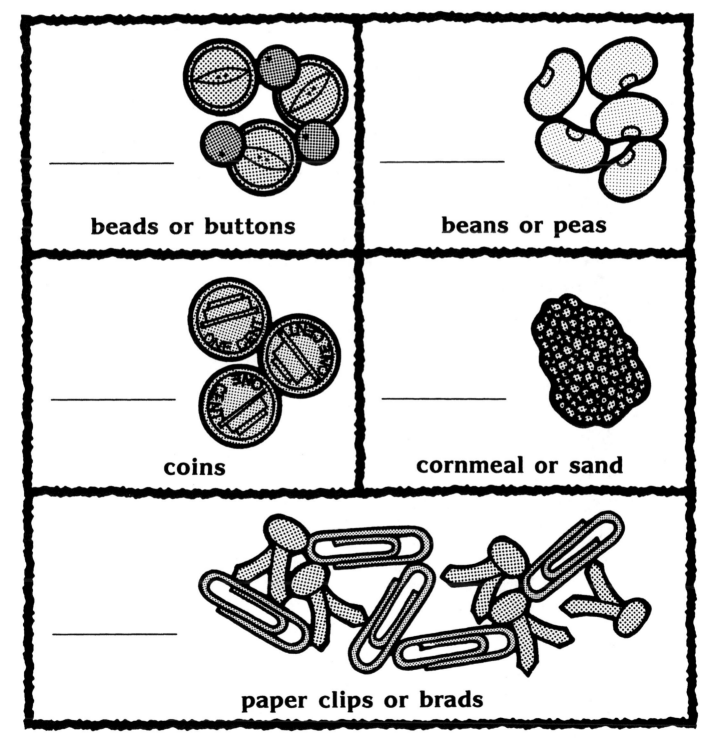

beads or buttons

beans or peas

coins

cornmeal or sand

paper clips or brads

How Do You Smell?

You smell with your **nose**. When you breathe, you draw air into your nose. Inside your nose are hairlike **nerve ends**. The air coming into your nose passes over these nerve ends. Some nerve ends notice the smell of chicken soup in the air. Other nerve ends notice the smell of cinnamon or sour milk.

The nerve ends send messages to your **brain**. Your brain thinks about these messages. It decides what you are smelling. It decides whether the smells are good or bad.

nose

smell

What Do You Smell?

What You Need

- at least six empty containers with tight-fitting lids (You can use film canisters, margarine tubs, empty spice jars, or Zip-loc bags.)
- six things that can be identified by smell (For example, you might use chocolate candy, ground or stick cinnamon, a garlic bud, shelled peanuts or peanut butter, a slice of ginger root, and a slice of lemon.)
- a clean white handkerchief to use as a blindfold

What You Do

1. Put one thing that smells in each container and close it tightly.

2. Blindfold a child.

3. One at a time, open the containers and pass them under the child's nose.

4. Caution the child to sniff lightly, *not* breathe deeply.

5. Ask the child to identify the smell.

6. If the child hesitates, give him or her a hint by asking, *Do you smell cinnamon or garlic? Do you smell ginger or lemon?*

7. Let the child—and the nose—rest between different smells.

Name _____

I Smell Dinner!

Someone is cooking your favorite dinner for your birthday. Write a story about all of the good smells that are coming from your kitchen. Make the reader wish that he or she had been invited to dinner.

_____

_____

_____

_____

_____

_____

_____

How Do You Taste?

You taste with your **tongue**. Stand in front of a mirror. Stick out your tongue. Notice that it is covered with bumps.

Inside these bumps are **taste buds**. The taste buds for **sweet** things are on the front of your tongue. The taste buds for **salty** and **sour** things are on the sides of your tongue. The taste buds for **bitter** things are on the back of your tongue.

Taste buds are really bunches of **taste nerves**. When you eat, these nerves send messages to your brain. Your **brain** thinks about these messages. It notices which taste buds they came from. It decides whether a taste is sweet or sour, salty or bitter. It also decides whether the taste is one you like or dislike.

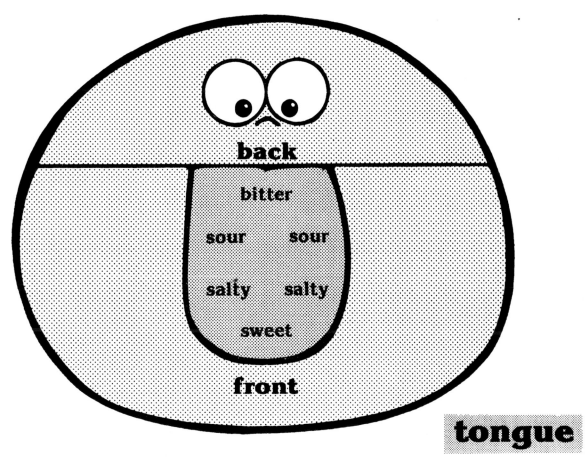

back

bitter

sour   sour

salty   salty

sweet

front

tongue

Name _____

A Yucky Taste

Think of a food you dislike. Write about how this food tastes. What does this taste remind you of?

_____

_____

_____

_____

_____

_____

_____

Name _____

Flavor Fun

Your tongue can recognize only four tastes. These tastes are sweet, salty, sour, and bitter.

Not all sweet foods taste alike. Both chocolate ice cream and strawberry ice cream are sweet. But you know which is which. And you know which one you like best.

The reason you can tell the difference between the flavors of these two sweet foods is your nose. You not only *taste* these flavors. You also *smell* them. Your nose helps you tell the difference between sweet foods. It helps you tell the difference between salty ones, sour ones, and bitter ones also.

Take a vote to find out which flavors your classmates like best. First, read the list of flavors so your classmates will know what their choices are. Next, read the names of these flavors one at a time. Ask the boys and girls to hold up their hands when they hear the names of their favorite flavors. Tell them to vote only once.

Each time you read the name of a flavor, count the number of hands. Write that number in the box beside the flavor name.

Flavors

1. almond	☐	6. coconut	☐	11. orange	☐
2. banana	☐	7. grape	☐	12. peppermint	☐
3. butterscotch	☐	8. lemon	☐	13. strawberry	☐
4. cherry	☐	9. licorice	☐	14. vanilla	☐
5. chocolate	☐	10. marshmallow	☐		

Name _____

Flavor Favorites

Use the results of your vote to make a graph. Color each flavor row to show the number of votes that flavor got. Which flavor was your class favorite? Is that flavor your favorite?

Flavors

1. almond
2. banana
3. butterscotch
4. cherry
5. chocolate
6. coconut
7. grape
8. lemon
9. licorice
10. marshmallow
11. orange
12. peppermint
13. strawberry
14. vanilla

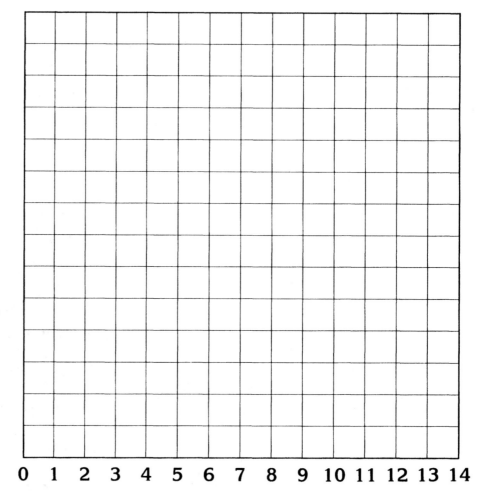

0 1 2 3 4 5 6 7 8 9 10 11 12 13 14

How Do You Think?

You think with your **brain**. Your brain thinks about what your eyes see. Your brain thinks about what your ears hear. Your brain thinks about what your nose smells. And your brain thinks about what your tongue tastes.

Your brain is very small. It weighs only about three pounds. Yet it can do more than the biggest computer ever built. It thinks. It learns. It remembers. And it makes all parts of your body work together.

Your brain has three main parts. These parts are the cerebrum, cerebellum, and brain stem.

The **cerebrum** (se-REE-brum) is the largest and most important part of your brain. Everything you have learned is stored in your cerebrum. All of your ideas and feelings come from this part of your brain.

Your **cerebellum** (ser-uh-BEL-um) sits under the back part of your cerebrum. It helps you move and keep your balance.

The smallest part of your brain is the **brain stem**. Parts of the brain stem control your body temperature. They also keep your stomach, heart, and lungs working so your cerebrum doesn't have to think about them.

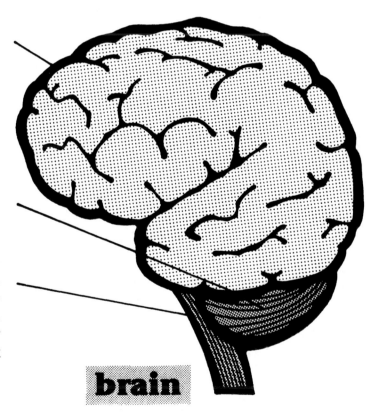

brain

Name _____

Follow the Dots

Follow these numbered dots to find something
your brain thinks about.

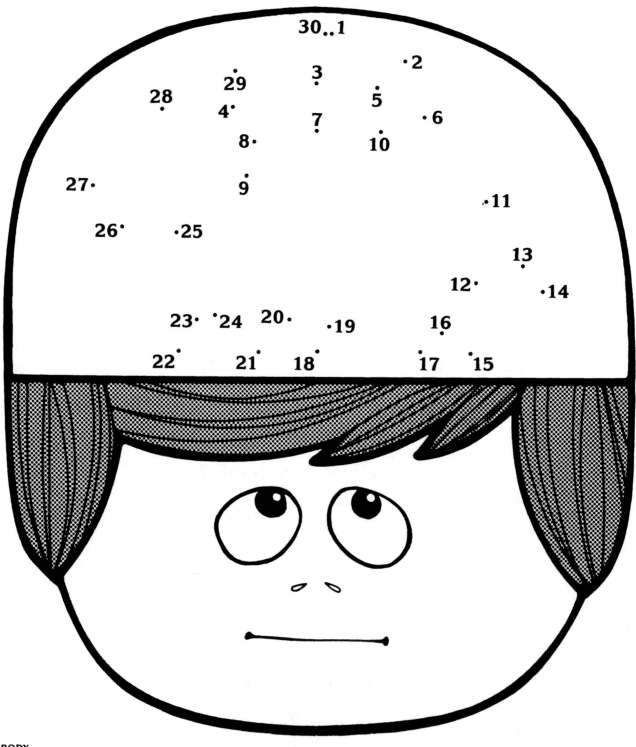

How Do You Chew?

You chew with your **teeth**. They bite and grind the food you eat. Without teeth, you could not eat apples, carrots, or nuts.

Your teeth are covered with **enamel** (ee-NAM-ul). The enamel protects your teeth and makes them look shiny and white.

Under the enamel is a very hard layer of **dentin** (DEN-tin). Inside the dentin layer is some spongy stuff called **pulp**.

Your teeth may look like they are just sitting on top of your **gums**, but they are not. They have **roots** that go down into your gums. Inside each root is a **nerve**. Sometimes, when you eat or drink something very cold, the nerve in a tooth hurts. If you feel pain in a tooth at other times, you should see a dentist.

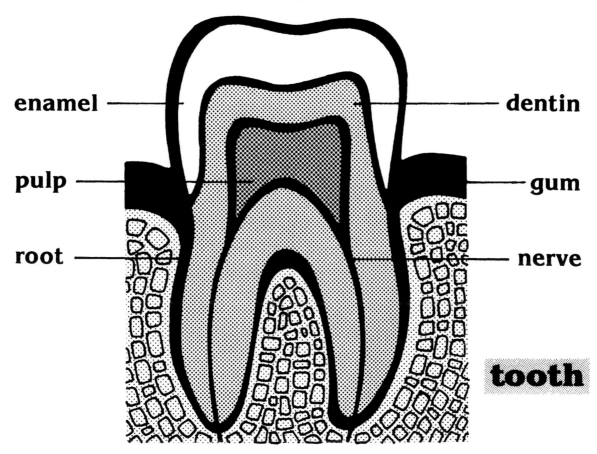

enamel — dentin

pulp — gum

root — nerve

tooth

Name _____

Crossword Fun

Read pages 13, 17, 27, and 29 carefully. Use what you learn and the clues below to complete these crossword puzzles.

Without teeth, you could not eat

Your teeth are covered with a coating called

The very hard layer under this coating is called

Teeth do not sit on the gums. They are held in place by

Sometimes cold things make your teeth

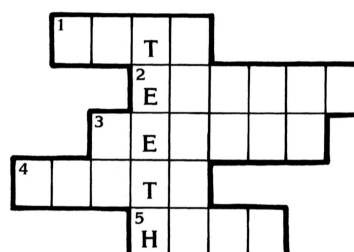

You use your ears to

You see with your

You think with your

Sound waves bump against your

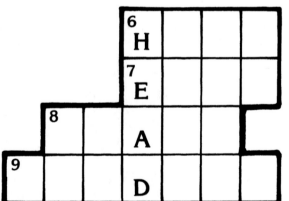

What's Inside Your Trunk?

Inside your trunk are many soft parts that work hard to keep you healthy and strong. These parts work even when you play. They help you get oxygen from the air you breathe. They help you get energy from the food you eat. They help you get rid of the air and food your body has used and doesn't need anymore.

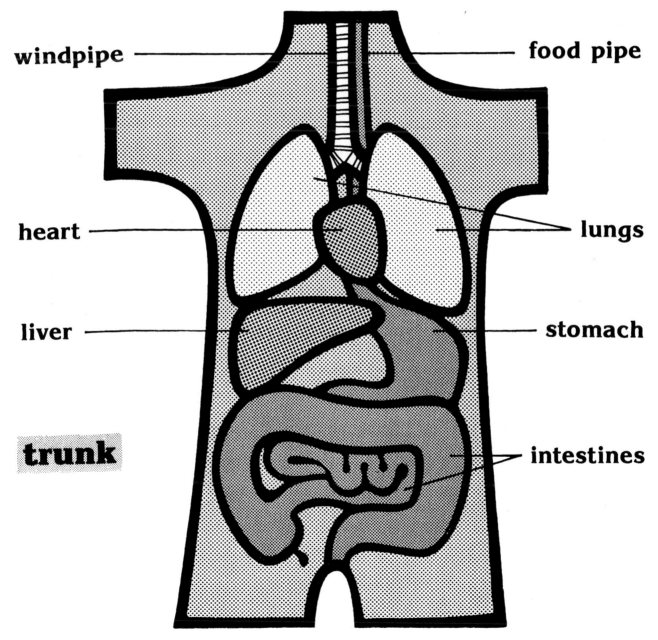

windpipe —————————— food pipe

heart ————— lungs

liver ————— stomach

trunk

intestines

What Does Your Heart Do?

Your **heart** pumps blood to all parts of your body. Your heart is found in the middle of your chest. It is about the same size as your fist.

Your heart is hollow. It is filled with blood. It is made of strong, tough muscle.

Muscle is a special kind of material that can tighten and then relax. When your heart muscle tightens, the space inside your heart gets smaller. The blood in this space is squeezed out to the rest of your body.

Did You Know?

1. Your heart is a little muscle with a big job.
2. It weighs less than a pound.
3. What we call a **heartbeat** is really your heart muscle tightening.
4. When you are sitting still, your heart beats about 90 times a minute.
5. At this rate, your heart beats more than 100,000 times each day!

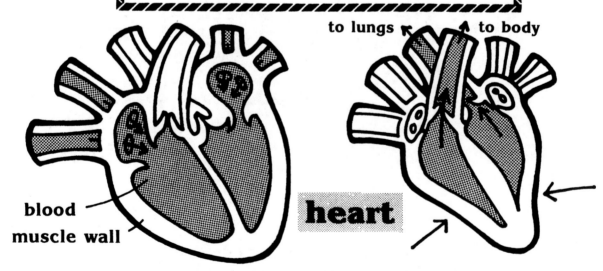

to lungs   to body

blood
muscle wall

heart

The strong muscle of the heart wall squeezes to push blood out of your heart. This blood goes to your lungs and to the rest of your body.

How Does Your Blood Flow?

The blood in your body **circulates**. This means that it goes around and around inside.

Your blood actually makes two round trips, a short trip and a long one. On the short trip, your blood flows from your heart to your lungs and back to your heart. On the long trip, it flows from your heart to your head, hands, and feet, and back to your heart.

The blood circulating in your body travels inside special tubes. These tubes are called **blood vessels**. The vessels that carry blood away from your heart are called **arteries**. The vessels that carry blood back to your heart are called **veins**.

blood vessels

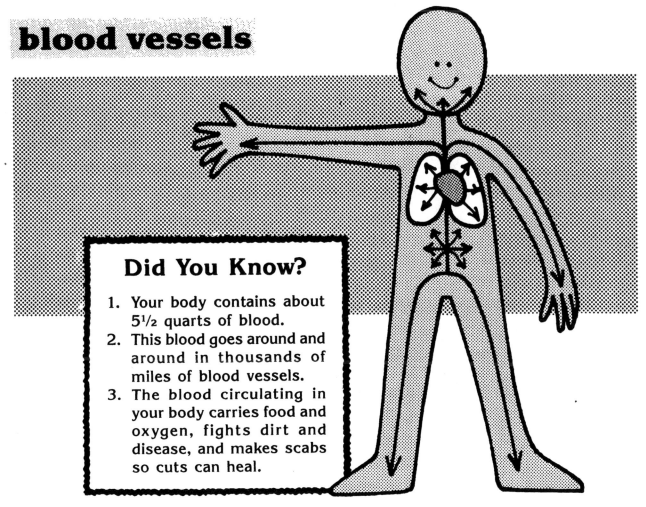

Did You Know?

1. Your body contains about 5½ quarts of blood.
2. This blood goes around and around in thousands of miles of blood vessels.
3. The blood circulating in your body carries food and oxygen, fights dirt and disease, and makes scabs so cuts can heal.

What Is Your Pulse?

Your **pulse** is the regular throbbing of blood in your arteries each time your heart beats. Because you cannot put your ear on your chest, you cannot easily hear your own heart beat. But you can *feel* your heart beat by resting two fingers lightly on an artery. The best places to do this are

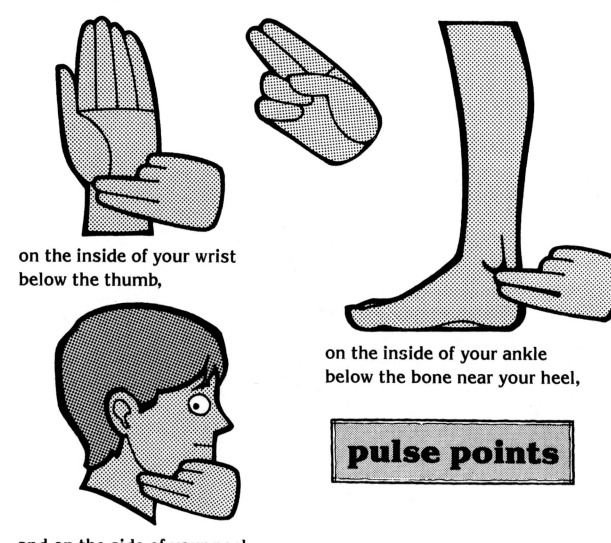

on the inside of your wrist
below the thumb,

on the inside of your ankle
below the bone near your heel,

pulse points

and on the side of your neck
under your jaw.

Find one of these pulse points and feel your heart beat.

Name _____

Feel the Beat

Your heart is amazing. It always beats at the speed you need. When you play hard, it beats very fast. When you sit still, it beats much slower. Find out how much faster your heart beats when you play hard.

1. Sit quietly for a while.
2. Find one of your pulse points. (See page 34.)
3. Rest two fingers lightly on this pulse point.
4. Ask someone to look at a clock or watch and time you for one minute.
5. During this minute, count the number of times you feel your heart beat.
6. Write the number of beats on **Line A** below.
7. Draw a line on the bar where this number should be.
8. Color the bar from the number 60 to the line you drew.
9. Run around or jump in place for a few minutes.
10. Stop and find your pulse point.
11. Again, count the number of times you feel your heart beat in one minute.
12. Write this number of beats on **Line B** below.
13. Draw a line on the bar where this number should be.
14. Color the bar from the number 60 to the line you drew.
15. Which number is larger, the one on **Line A** or the one on **Line B**?
16. Notice which colored bar is longer.

A. My heart beats _____ times each minute when I sit still.

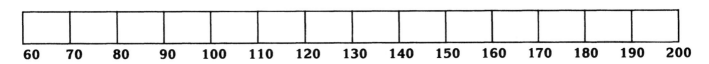

B. My heart beats _____ times each minute when I play hard.

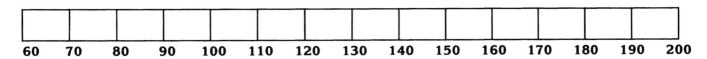

YOUR BODY

What Are Your Lungs?

Your **lungs** are two balloon-like bags in your chest. They help you breathe. When you draw air in through your nose or mouth, this air fills your lungs. In this air is something very important. It is called oxygen. **Oxygen** is a gas needed by all living things.

Your heart pumps blood to your lungs. This blood releases used air in the form of another gas, called **carbon dioxide**. The used air leaves your body when you breathe out.

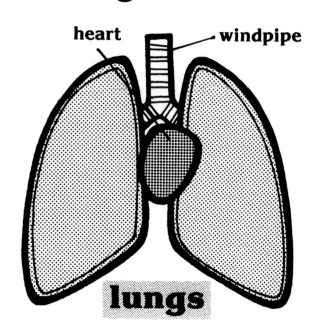

heart · windpipe

lungs

Have Some Fun Breathing

Breathe in
to smell a good
kitchen or garden smell.

Count the number of times
you breathe in and out
during one minute.

Breathe out
to blow
into a horn or whistle.

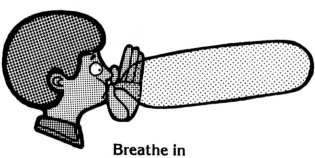

Breathe in
to fill your lungs.
Then breathe out
to blow up a balloon.

Breathe in
to fill your lungs.
Then breathe out
to blow out birthday candles.

Name _____

Body Parts Puzzle

The eighteen words listed in the box are the names of parts of your body. These words have been hidden in this puzzle. See how many of them you can find and circle. The word **ear** actually appears twice!

```
I  N  T  E  S  T  I  N  E  S
B  R  A  I  N  H  E  A  R  T
T  X  R  N  F  O  O  T  Z  O
E  L  T  M  O  U  T  H  E  M
E  U  E  N  O  E  E  Y  E  A
T  N  R  O  D  H  A  N  D  C
H  G  Y  S  P  H  R  B  N  H
O  S  A  E  I  H  E  A  D  T
W  I  N  D  P  I  P  E  H  E
M  L  I  V  E  R  V  E  I  N
```

Word Box

artery • brain • ear • eye • food pipe • foot
hand • head • heart • intestines • liver • lungs
mouth • nose • stomach • teeth • vein • windpipe

Bones and Muscles

Your **skeleton** is the framework that gives your body its basic shape. Your skeleton is made up of 206 separate pieces called **bones**. The places where these bones come together are called **joints**. Your elbow, wrist, knee, and ankle are joints.

Bones come in different sizes and shapes. The bones in your ear are tiny. One of them is shaped like a stirrup. The bones in your arms and legs are long. The bones in your wrist and ankles are short.

Muscles move all parts of your body by pulling and relaxing. They make your heart beat. They make your lungs breathe. They lift your arms and legs. Without muscles, you could not walk, run, jump, throw, catch, or climb.

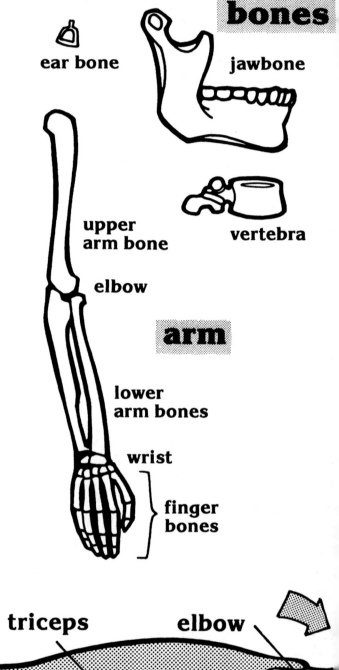

bones

ear bone

jawbone

upper arm bone

vertebra

elbow

arm

lower arm bones

wrist

finger bones

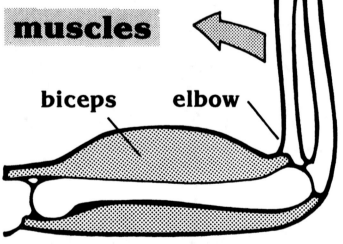

muscles

biceps   elbow

triceps   elbow

A muscle called the **biceps** pulls your forearm up.

A muscle called the **triceps** pulls your forearm down.

Fascinating Facts About Your Body

Water makes up about 65 percent of your body.

Your heart beats about 100,000 times each day.

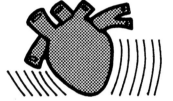

An **organ** is a specialized part of your body. Your heart, your lungs, and your eyes are organs. Your skin is the largest organ in your body.

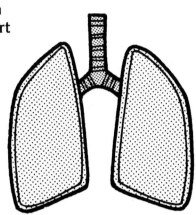

The largest bone in your body is found in your upper leg.

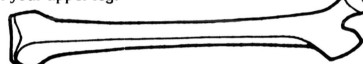

The smallest bone in your body is found in your middle ear.

The outer surface of your brain is made up of more than 8 million cells.

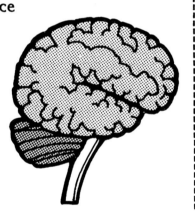

The **pupil** of your eye can change size.

When you enter a dark room, it gets larger, or **dilates**, to let in more light.

When you go out in bright sunlight, it gets smaller, or **constricts**, to let in less light.

Your body's cells wear out and must be replaced. Every 15 to 30 days, your body replaces your entire outer layer of skin.

The heart of a 70-year-old person has pumped about 46 million gallons of blood during that person's lifetime.

Human Body Clip Art

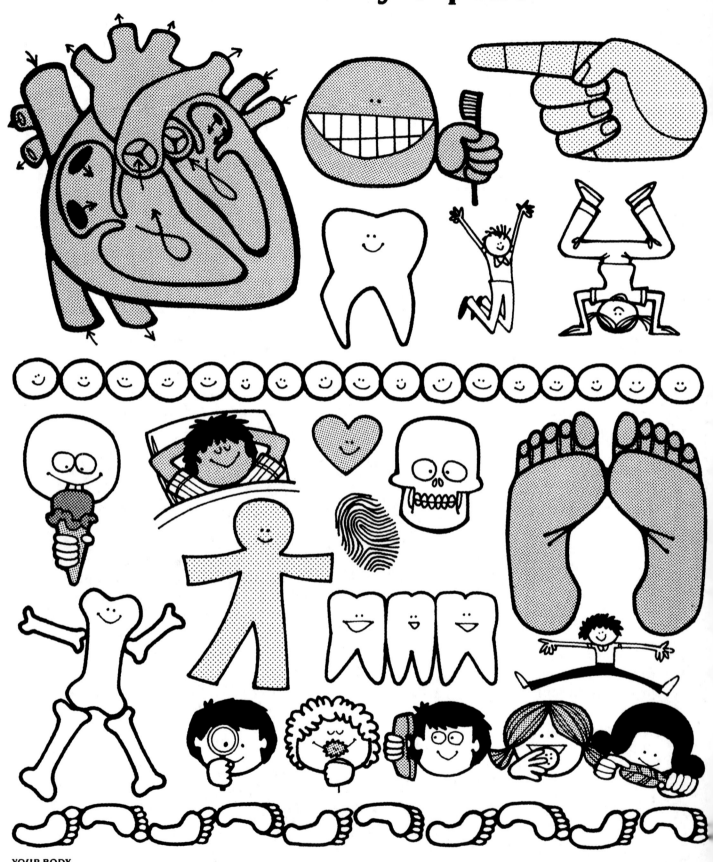

Name _____

Teeth to Try

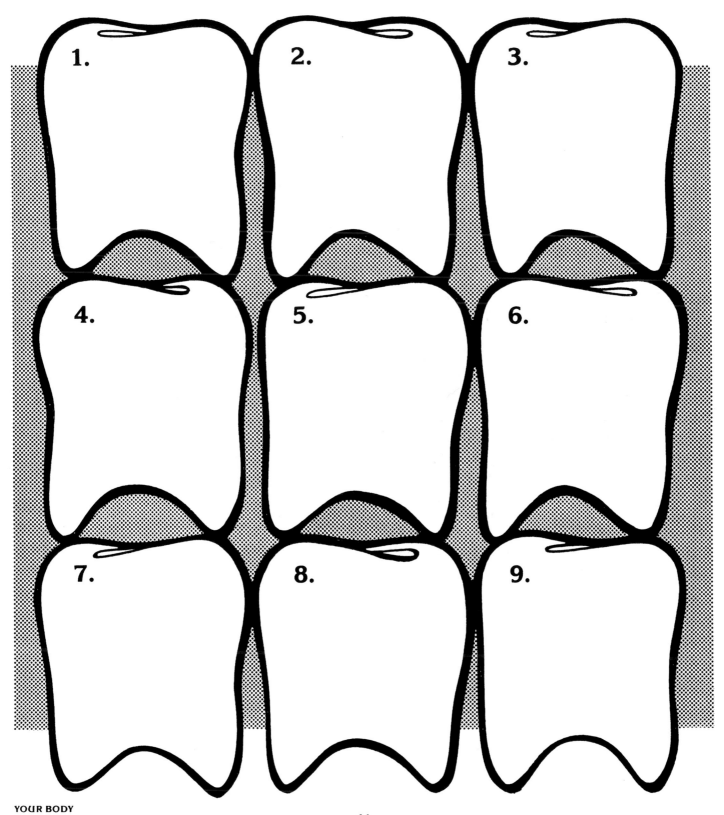

A Few Words About Your Body

arteries — The tubes that carry blood from your heart to the rest of your body (page 33).

blood vessels — Tubes in which blood travels throughout your body. Both arteries and veins are blood vessels (page 33).

brain — The part of your body that thinks, learns, and remembers. Your brain guides your movements and makes sense of what you see, hear, smell, and taste (pages 27 and 39).

brain stem — The smallest part of your brain, which controls your body temperature and keeps your heart, lungs, and stomach working while you sleep or play (page 27).

carbon dioxide — Odorless, colorless used air from your body, which you get rid of when you breathe out (page 36).

cerebellum — The part of your brain that helps you move your muscles and keep your balance (page 27).

cerebrum — The largest and most important part of your brain. All of your ideas and feelings come from your cerebrum (page 27).

dentin — The hard bony material that makes up the main part of a tooth (page 29).

eardrum — The part of your ear that vibrates when sound waves bump against it (page 17).

enamel — The coating that protects your teeth and makes them look shiny and white (page 29).

food pipe — The tube that carries the food you swallow down your throat to your stomach. It is also called the esophagus (eh-SAF-uh-gus) (pages 8 and 31).

heart — A hollow muscle that beats about 100,000 times each day and pumps blood to all parts of your body (pages 31, 32, and 39).

joint — The place in your body where one bone is connected to another bone (page 38).

A Few Words About Your Body
(continued)

lens   The part of your eye that collects light and points it toward your retina (page 13).

lungs   The two balloon-like bags in your chest which fill with air when you breathe in (page 36).

muscle   A special kind of material that moves parts of your body by first tightening and then relaxing (pages 32 and 38).

nerve   A fiber that carries messages from your body to your brain (page 13); the fiber inside each tooth root which is sensitive to cold, heat, and pain (page 29).

oxygen   An odorless, colorless gas that is needed by all living things and is found in the air you breathe (page 36).

pinna   The outer part of your ear which catches sound waves that are in the air (page 17).

pulp   The spongy stuff inside your teeth (page 29).

pulse   The regular throbbing of blood in your arteries each time your heart beats (page 34).

pupil   The small black hole through which light enters your eye. It constricts in bright sunlight and dilates in a dark room (page 13 and 39).

retina   The back part of your eyeball, which is sensitive to light (page 13).

skeleton   The framework formed by the bones of your body (page 38).

taste buds The tiny bundles of nerves on the surface of your tongue which are sensitive to taste (page 23).

veins   The tubes that carry blood from your body back to your heart (page 33).

vocal cords Membranes at the top of your windpipe that produce sounds when they are vibrated by your outgoing breath (page 8).

windpipe   The tube that carries the air you breathe down your throat to your lungs. It is also called the trachea (TRAY-kee-uh).

_____
(name of student)

has recently completed a unit of study
entitled

Your Body

and is hereby
presented
an

Anatomy Awareness Award

in recognition of this accomplishment.

_____
(signature of teacher)

_____
(date)

Special Human Body Awards

Thanks,

_____.

You
have a kind

heart!

Make no bones
about it!

_____,

you're super!

You are showing
strong improvement
in

_____!

Keep up
the good work!

_____,

I see

you are doing
much better in

_____.

Special Human Body Awards
(continued)

Did you hear
the good news?

_____

did well in

_____ .

Your good work
put a smile

on my
face!

Good for you,

_____ !

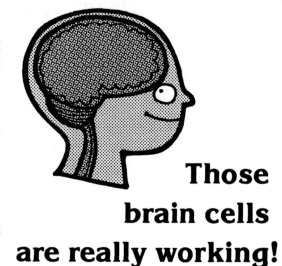

Those
brain cells
are really working!

Thank you for
lending a
hand!

Correlated Activities
(for kids to do with adult help)

1. Your normal body temperature is about 98.6 degrees on a Fahrenheit thermometer. It may be a little lower when you first get up and a little higher after you have been playing. With help, use a thermometer to take and read your temperature several times during one day. As you do so, write down the temperature readings. At the end of the day, notice whether these readings are exactly the same or slightly different. **(Observing and Comparing)**

2. Your body has 206 bones. These bones have easy names like jawbone, collarbone, breastbone, and knee-cap. They also have hard names like **mandible, clavicle, sternum**, and **patella**. Just for fun, look up and learn some of these hard names. Be able to point to each bone as you name it. **(Identifying and Labeling)**

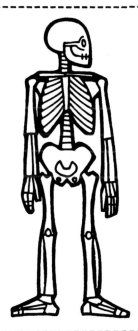

3. A **stethoscope** is something doctors use to listen to hearts beat and lungs breathe. Borrow a stethoscope and listen to your own heart and lungs in action. **(Experiencing)**

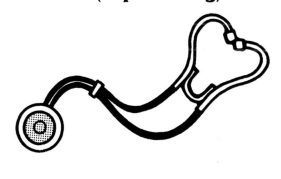

4. Different parts of your body need special care to stay healthy. For example, your heart and lungs need exercise, and your teeth need to be brushed. First, learn more about how to take care of some part of your body. Then, create a poster to share what you have learned with your classmates. **(Understanding Concepts and Communicating Ideas)**

5. Look closely at the tips of your fingers. The skin on them is covered with tiny ridges. When you touch something, these ridges leave a pattern, which is called a **fingerprint**. Nobody in the world has a set of fingerprints exactly like yours. Use your special fingerprints to create some critters. First, wash and dry your hands. Next, roll your thumb or fingers against an inked pad. Then, press your inked thumb or fingers onto white paper. Finally, use a felt-tipped pen to turn your fingerprints into critters. **(Crafts and Creativity)**

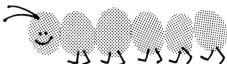

Answer Key

Page 7, About Face
1.
smiling face

2.
frowning face

Page 9, Sounds the Same
a. face
e. teeth
i. smile
o. foot

Page 11, Which Is Longer?
Individual answers may vary, but expected proportions are as follows:
1. Your leg is longer than your arm.
2. Your leg is longer than your trunk.
3. Your forearm and foot are approximately the same.
4. Your thumb is longer than your big toe.
5. Your foot is longer than your hand.

Page 14, Tricky Pictures
The center circles are the same size.
The four lines are the same length.
The height and width of the hat are the same.

Page 18–19, What Do You Hear?
Answers will vary according to container contents and numbers.

Page 21, What Do You Smell?
Answers will vary according to container contents.

Page 25, Flavor Fun
Numbers in boxes will vary.

Page 26, Flavor Favorites
Graphs will vary according to the numbers obtained in the survey on page 25.

Page 28, Follow the Dots
When the dots are connected in numerical order, the result is a picture of a rabbit.

Page 30, Crossword Fun
1. nuts
2. enamel
3. dentin
4. roots
5. hurt
6. hear
7. eyes
8. brain
9. eardrum

Page 35, Feel the Beat
Individual heartbeat/pulse rate graphs will vary, but the heart of a normal child beats about 90 times a minute.

Page 37, Body Parts Puzzle

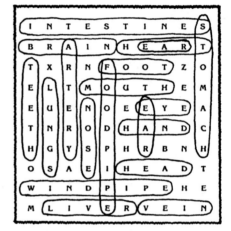